One more, one less

4								
14								
24	25							
34	35	36						
44	45	46						
54	55	56	57	58	59	60	61	6
64	65	66	67	68	69	70	71	7
74	75	76	77	78	79	80	81	8
84	85	86	87	88	89	90	91	9

☐ 76 77

☐ 85 ☐

☐ 57 ☐

☐ 32 ☐

☐ 68 ☐

☐ 16 ☐

☐ 43 ☐

☐ 29 ☐

☐ 91 ☐

☐ 30 ☐

☐ 99 ☐

Use a 100-square. Colour a number red. Colour the number one more blue. Repeat.

Write the number one more. Write the number one less.

Work with a partner. Say a number. They say the number 10 more; you say 10 less. Swap roles.

More and less

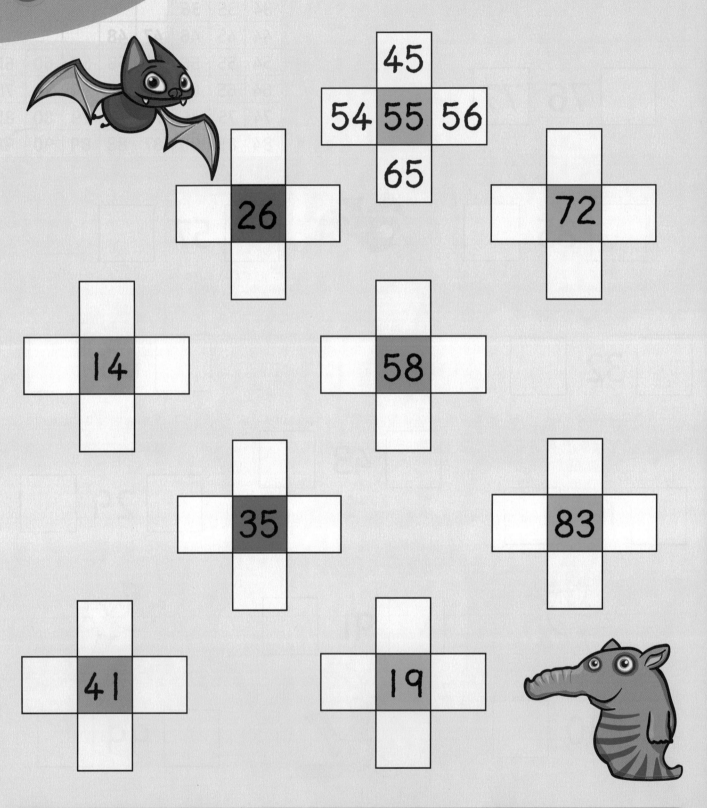

Use a 100-square. Colour a number red. Colour the numbers 10 more and 10 less yellow. Repeat.

Write the numbers 10 more and 10 less; and one more and one less.

Copy one of these crosses. What is the pattern of the numbers that fit in the diagonals?

Counting objects

Take a handful of puzzle pieces. Guess how many, then count.

Count the puzzle pieces. How many pieces have fish on? Have shells on? Have yellow on? Have red on?

Look at how many pieces have fish. How many do not have fish? Do you need to count?

Counting objects

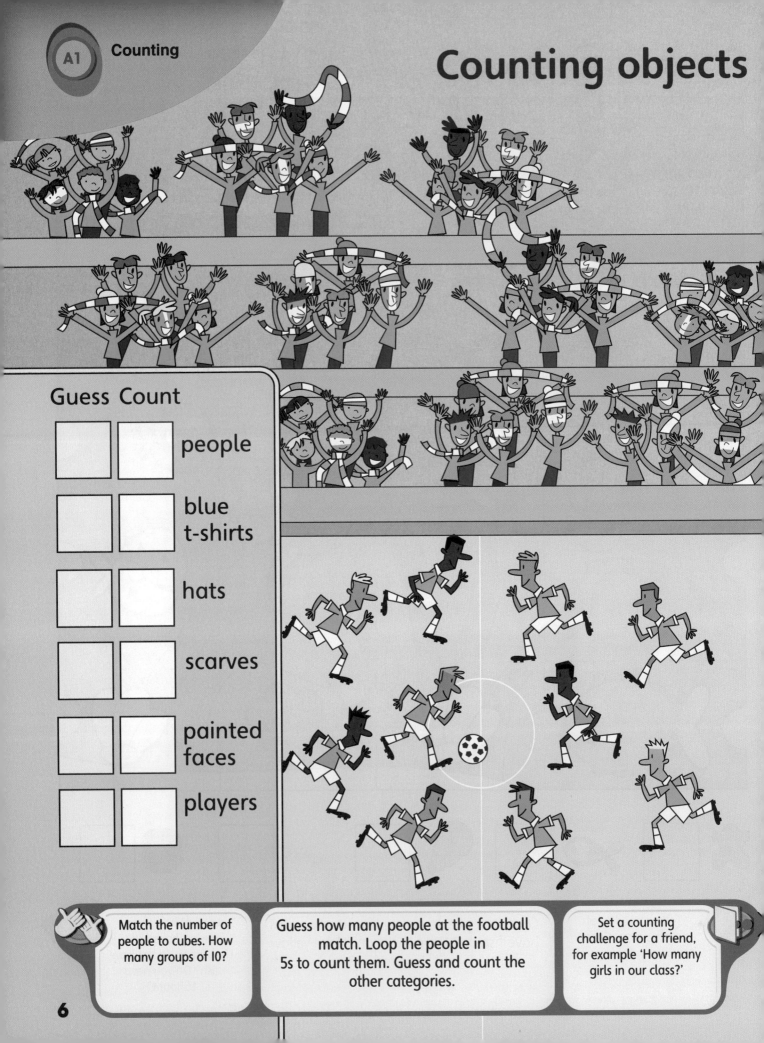

Guess Count

Guess	Count	
		people
		blue t-shirts
		hats
		scarves
		painted faces
		players

Match the number of people to cubes. How many groups of 10?

Guess how many people at the football match. Loop the people in 5s to count them. Guess and count the other categories.

Set a counting challenge for a friend, for example 'How many girls in our class?'

Tens and units

 2

 7 0

 8 0

86

93

72

36

 6

52

44

97

 3

 9 0

50

43

 5 0

 4

57

34

 3 0

 7

 4 0

 Use place value cards to make the numbers in the centre of the page.

Match the place value cards to the numbers in the centre of the page.

What card do you need to add to each number to make the next multiple of 10? For example 86 + 4.

Tens and units

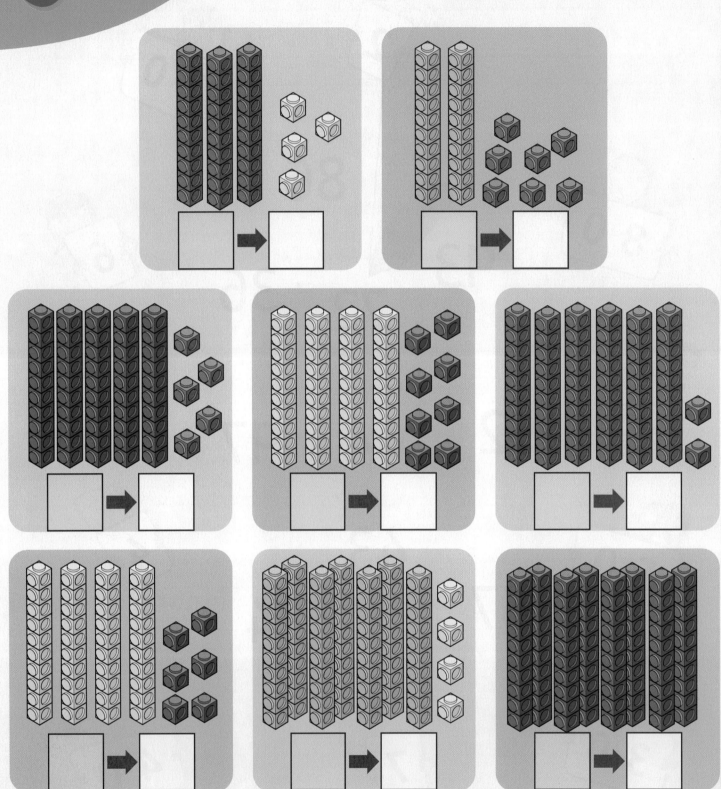

Use a 100-square. Place a counter on each number shown here.

Write the number of cubes in each set in the blue box. Add one tower of 10 and one cube. Write the new number of cubes.

Which numbers would have twice as many towers as cubes? Twice as many cubes as towers?

Tens and units

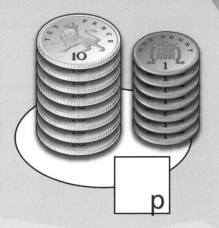

[   ] p

[   ] p

 52p

37p

55p

46p

16p

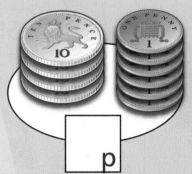

[   ] p

87p

64p

43p

[   ] p

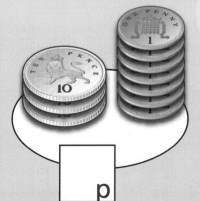

[   ] p

[   ] p

[   ] p

How many coins do you need to make each amount?

Join each pile of coins to an amount. Write the amount that is 10p less below each pile.

You have 13 coins (10p and 1p coins). What amounts could you have?

9

Ordering numbers

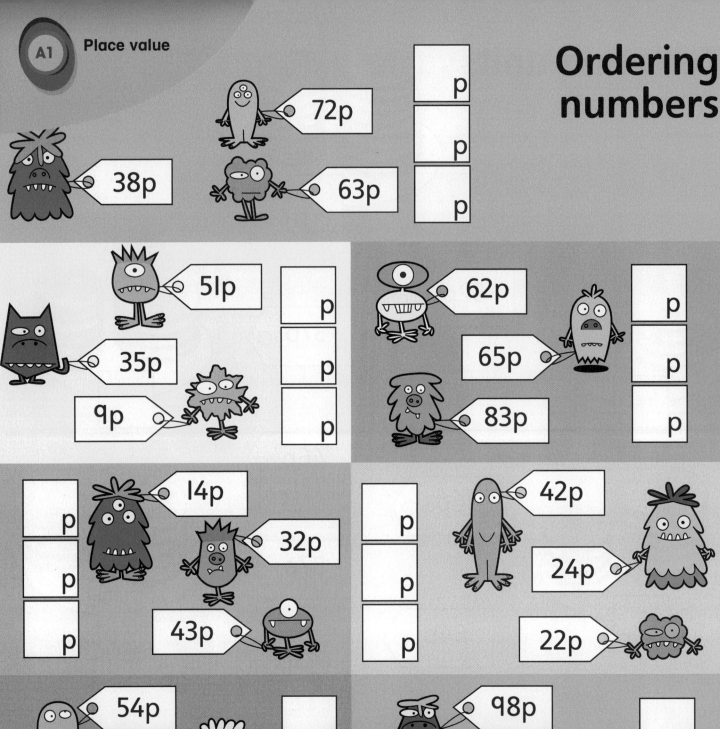

Use coins to help you find the largest amount in each group.

Write the prices in each group in order, from smallest to largest.

Write a number. Reverse its digits. Write a number between these two. Repeat.

Ordering numbers

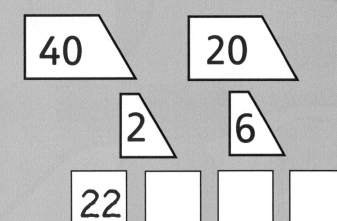

40   20

2   6

22 ☐ ☐ ☐

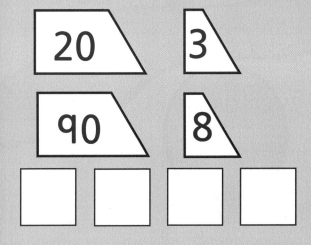

8   3

30   80

☐ ☐ ☐ ☐

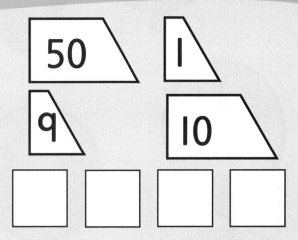

50   1

9   10

☐ ☐ ☐ ☐

20   3

90   8

☐ ☐ ☐ ☐

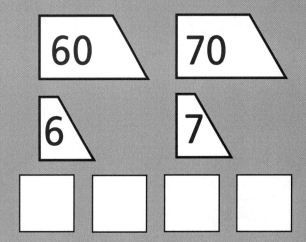

60   70

6   7

☐ ☐ ☐ ☐

Find each of these numbers on a 100-square. Cover them with counters.

Use pairs of place value cards to make four different numbers. Write them in order, from smallest to largest.

Place all the numbers on the page in order. Which is nearest the middle?

Counting on

11 + 2

14 + 2

9 7 8 9 10 11 12 13 14 15 16

9 + 2

7 + 1

15 + 1

19 + 1

22 + 2

24 + 2

20 19 21 22 23 24 25 26 27 28 29 30 31

25 + 1

27 + 2

30 + 2

Choose an addition. Make the numbers using cube towers.

Use the number tracks to help you complete each addition.

Write six different additions with an answer of 15.

Counting on

11
12
13
14
15
16
17
18
19
20
21
22
23
24
25
26
27
28
29
30
31
32
33
34
35
36
37
38
39
40
41
42
43
44
45
46
47
48
49
50

14 + 5 = ☐

12 + 7 = ☐

32 + 9 = ☐

42 + 6 = ☐

45 + 5 = ☐

16 + 6 = ☐

24 + 7 = ☐

26 + 3 = ☐

35 + 6 = ☐

48 + 5 = ☐

Place counters on the number track to help you complete each addition.

Complete the additions. Use the number track to help you.

Choose numbers that end in 6. Add 5. What is the pattern?

13

Adding

36 + 6

$36 + \boxed{} = 40$

$36 + 6 = \boxed{}$

27 + 5

$27 + \boxed{} = 30$

$27 + 5 = \boxed{}$

47 + 5

$47 + \boxed{} = 50$

$47 + 5 = \boxed{}$

48 + 6

$48 + \boxed{} = 50$

$48 + 6 = \boxed{}$

58 + 4

$58 + \boxed{} = 60$

$58 + 4 = \boxed{}$

69 + 6

$69 + \boxed{} = 70$

$69 + 6 = \boxed{}$

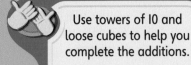

Use towers of 10 and loose cubes to help you complete the additions.

Write the missing numbers to complete the additions.

Write additions where the number added is 8 and the answer ends in 1.

Adding

18 + 5 + 2 = ☐

34 + 2 + 1 = ☐

24 + 5 + 1 = ☐

45 + 3 + 2 = ☐

38 + 6 + 4 = ☐

44 + 4 + 1 = ☐

29 + 4 + 2 = ☐

31 + 6 + 3 = ☐

| Make each score using towers of 10 and loose cubes. | Add the scores from each set of judges. | Someone scores 100. What could the three score cards be? |

15

Adding

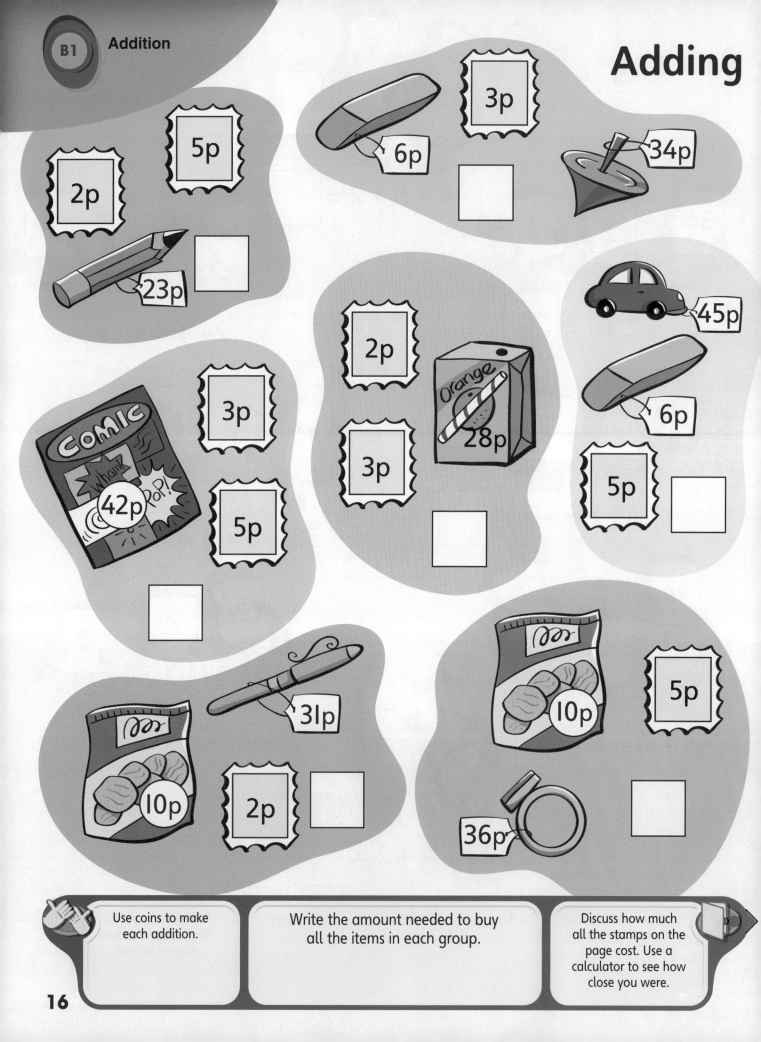

5p

2p

23p

6p

3p

34p

3p

45p

COMIC

whank

PoP!

42p

3p

5p

2p

3p

Orange

28p

6p

5p

31p

10p

2p

10p

5p

36p

Use coins to make each addition.

Write the amount needed to buy all the items in each group.

Discuss how much all the stamps on the page cost. Use a calculator to see how close you were.

16

Splitting 5 and 6

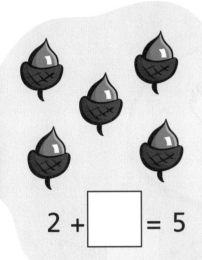

2 + ☐ = 5

1 + ☐ = 5

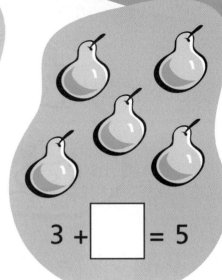

3 + ☐ = 5

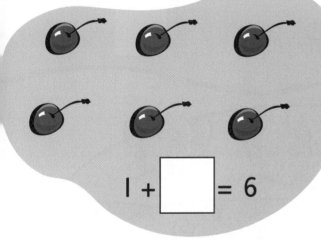

1 + ☐ = 6

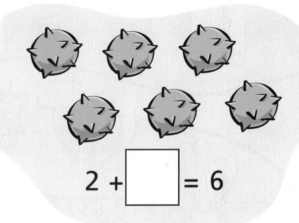

2 + ☐ = 6

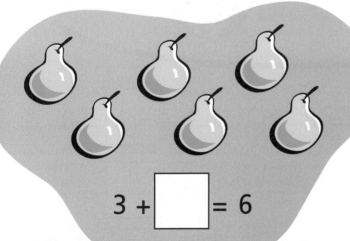

3 + ☐ = 6

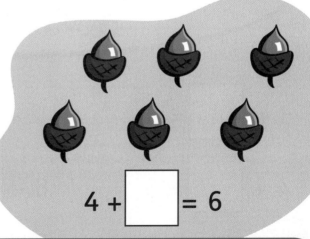

4 + ☐ = 6

 Make five Plasticene hedgehogs. Split them into two sets. Repeat.

Draw a line to split the set. Write the matching numbers in the addition.

How many ways can you find to split a set of six objects into three smaller sets?

17

Splitting 7 and 8

$0 + \boxed{} = 7$ $1 + \boxed{} = 7$ $2 + \boxed{} = 7$

$3 + \boxed{} = 7$ $7 - \boxed{} = 5$ $7 - \boxed{} = 1$

$1 + \boxed{} = 8$ $2 + \boxed{} = 8$ $3 + \boxed{} = 8$

$4 + \boxed{} = 8$ $8 - \boxed{} = 3$ $8 - \boxed{} = 2$

Use 0–8 number cards. Lay them down in pairs to make 8.

Write the missing numbers in the additions and subtractions.

Use your pairs to 7 to think of pairs that add to 17.

Splitting 9

0 + ☐

1 + ☐

☐ + 7

9

☐ + 6

5 + ☐

4 + ☐

☐ p + ☐ p = 9p

☐ p + ☐ p = 9p

☐ p + ☐ p = 9p

Use playing cards. Put pairs together that add to 9.

Write the missing numbers to complete the pairs to 9 in the flower. Complete the money additions.

In fours we collect chair legs, seasons... Find things we collect in fives... sixes...sevens.

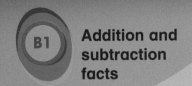
Adding to 10

$2 + \boxed{} = 10$

$1 + \boxed{} = 10$

$4 + \boxed{} = 10$

$3 + \boxed{} = 10$

$6 + \boxed{} = 10$

$5 + \boxed{} = 10$

$8 + \boxed{} = 10$

$7 + \boxed{} = 10$

$10 - \boxed{} = 7$

$9 + \boxed{} = 10$

$10 - \boxed{} = 4$

Thread 10 beads in two colours. How many different ways can you do this?

Write the missing numbers to complete the additions and subtractions.

How many ways can you find of making 10p using a 5p coin and other coins?

Adding to 10

4 + ☐ = 10

7 + ☐ = 10

2 + ☐ = 10

6 + ☐ = 10

3 + ☐ = 10

5 + ☐ = 10

9 + ☐ = 10

8 + ☐ = 10

 Split a tower of 10 cubes into two to show the pairs of scores.

How many more points to make 10?

Can you write all the pairs to 10 in 1 minute?

21

Length

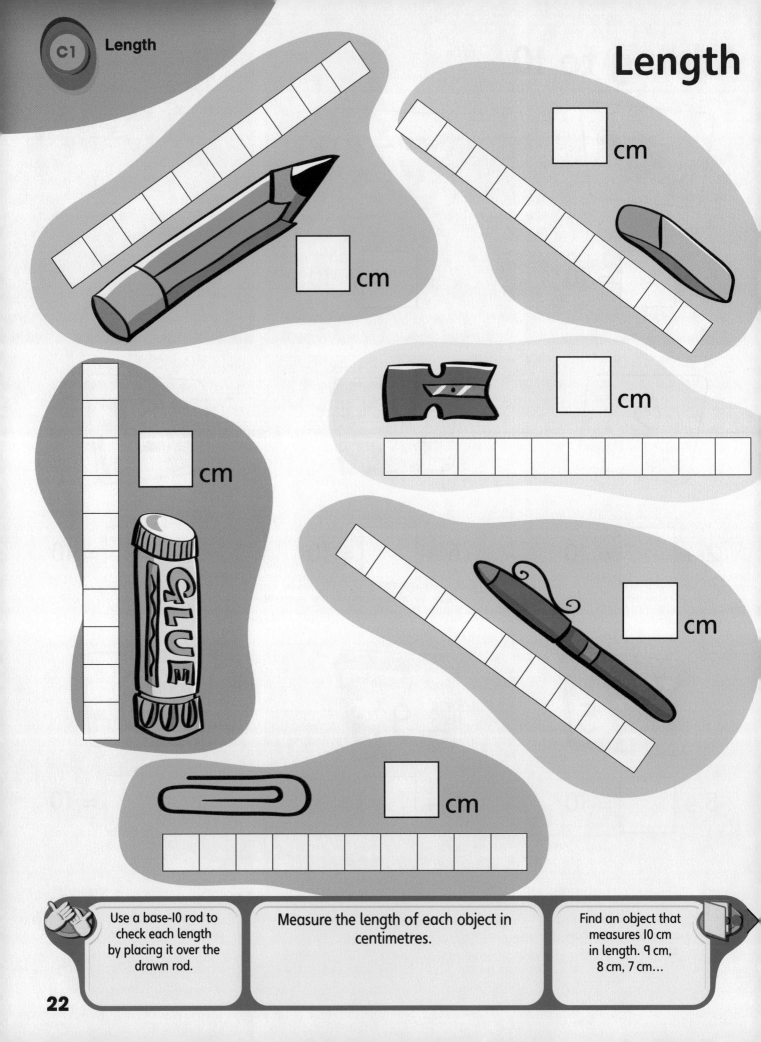

☐ cm

☐ cm

☐ cm

☐ cm

☐ cm

☐ cm

☐ cm

Use a base-10 rod to check each length by placing it over the drawn rod.

Measure the length of each object in centimetres.

Find an object that measures 10 cm in length. 9 cm, 8 cm, 7 cm...

Length

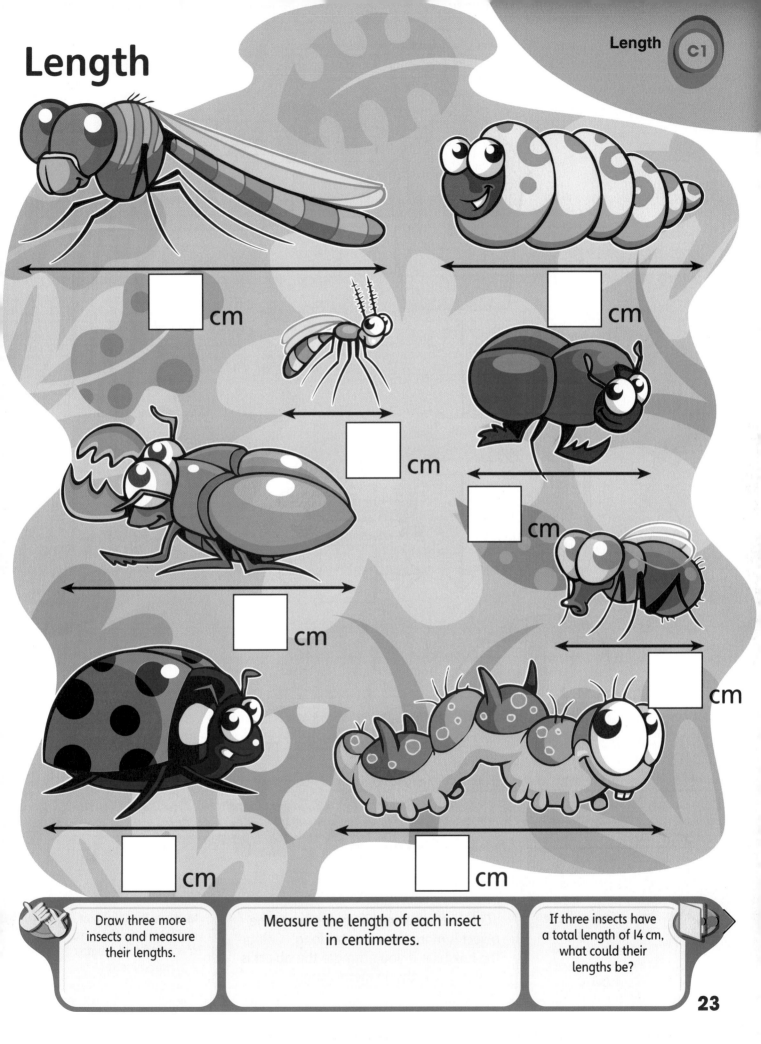

☐ cm

☐ cm

☐ cm

☐ cm

☐ cm

☐ cm

☐ cm

☐ cm

Draw three more insects and measure their lengths.

Measure the length of each insect in centimetres.

If three insects have a total length of 14 cm, what could their lengths be?

Length

Draw something else in this scene that is more or less than 1 metre long and label it.

Colour the box red if you estimate the object is more than 1 metre long. Colour the box blue if you estimate the object is less than 1 metre long.

Measure the length of your foot in centimetres. How many foot lengths make 1 metre?

Length

Make a line of cubes 1 metre long.

Write 'm' in the box if you would measure in metres. Write 'cm' in the box if you would measure in centimetres.

Measure the length of each of your fingers. If you could put them all in a line, how long would it be?

25

Days

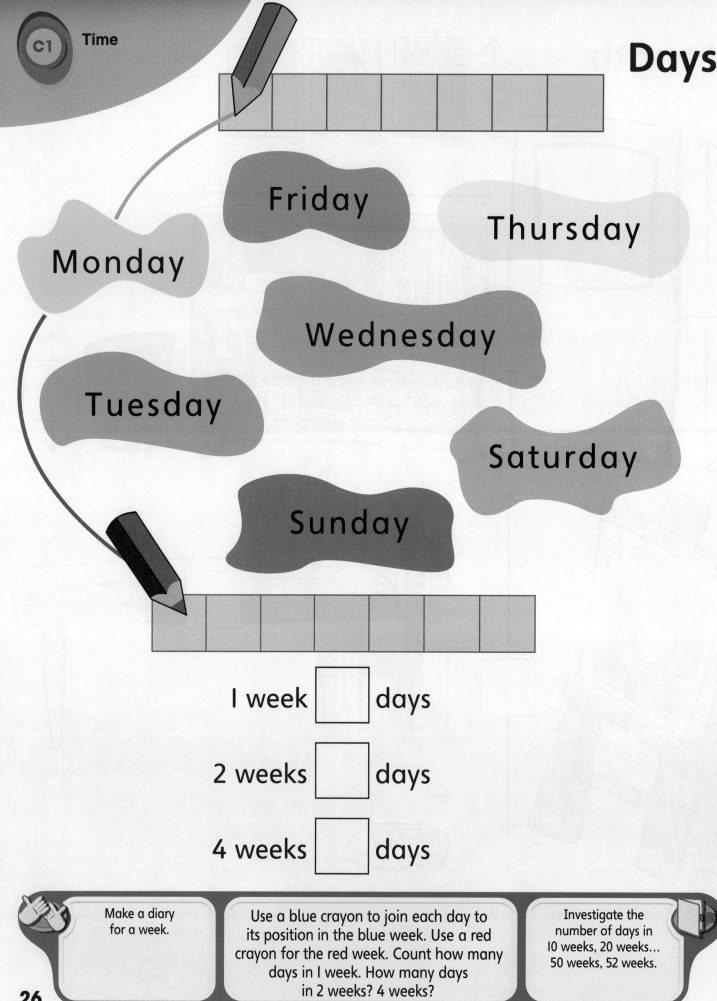

Friday

Thursday

Monday

Wednesday

Tuesday

Saturday

Sunday

1 week ☐ days

2 weeks ☐ days

4 weeks ☐ days

| Make a diary for a week. | Use a blue crayon to join each day to its position in the blue week. Use a red crayon for the red week. Count how many days in 1 week. How many days in 2 weeks? 4 weeks? | Investigate the number of days in 10 weeks, 20 weeks... 50 weeks, 52 weeks. |

Months and seasons

 Spring Summer

 Autumn Winter

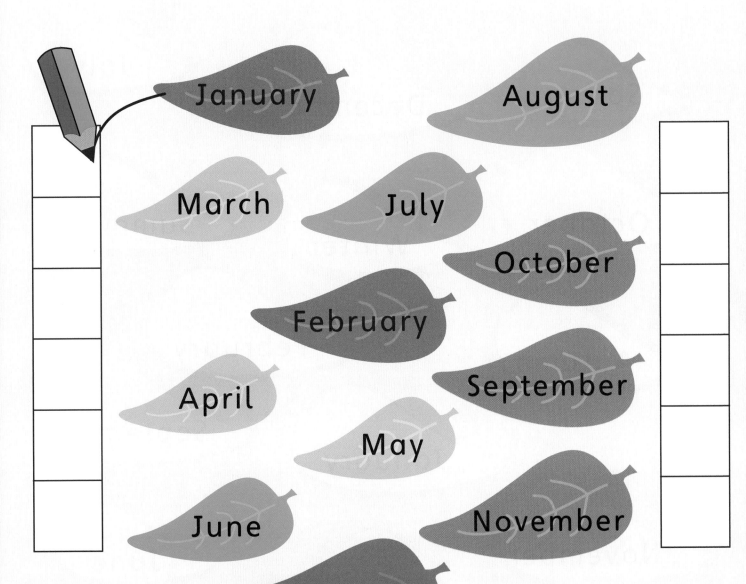

January

August

March

July

October

February

April

September

May

June

November

December

 Choose a month and draw a matching picture.

Join the months to the chart in order. Colour the boxes to match each season.

Investigate how many months you have lived.

27

Months and seasons

March

May

August

Spring

December

July

October

Winter

Summer

Autumn

February

January

September

November

April

June

Make a month calendar and write names of friends whose birthdays fall in different months.	Join each month to its season. Colour your birth month and its season. Colour the month before and after.	Investigate how many children in the class were 'summer babies', 'winter babies'...

Shape names

square   rectangle   triangle

pentagon   hexagon   octagon

Draw one shape to match each name.

Join all the shapes with the same name. Use the names to help you.

Find out the names of shapes with 7, 9 and 10 sides.

Shape names

rectangle

pentagon

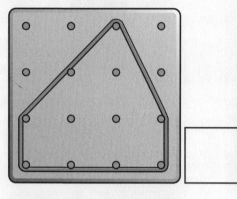

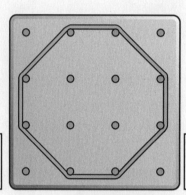

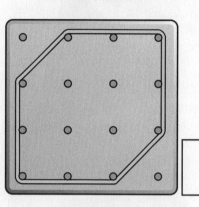

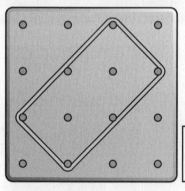

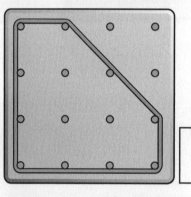

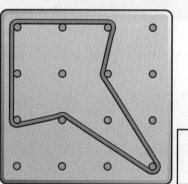

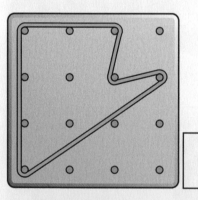

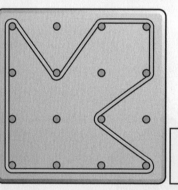

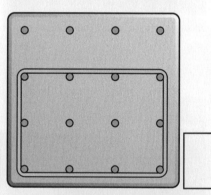

hexagon

octagon

 Make shapes using a rubber band on a pin-board. How many can you name?

Join each shape to its name. Write how many corners each shape has.

Investigate the different triangles you can make on a 4 x 4 pin-board.

Symmetry

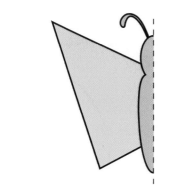

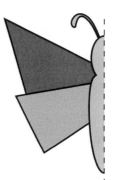

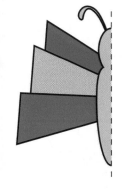

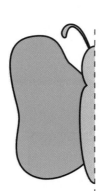

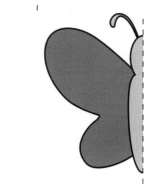

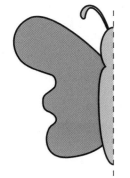

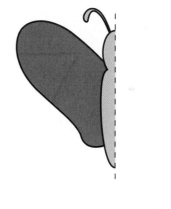

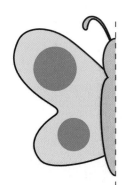

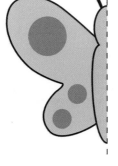

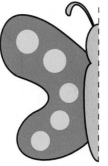

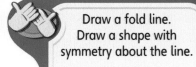
Draw a fold line. Draw a shape with symmetry about the line.

Each butterfly is symmetrical. Draw and colour the other half.

Make a list with a friend of all the symmetrical things you can think of.

31

Symmetry

Fold a piece of paper.
Cut out a shape.
Open it up.

Draw one line of symmetry on each shape.

Investigate which shapes have more than one line of symmetry.

Taking away

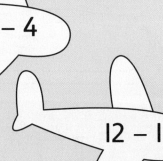

15 – 3

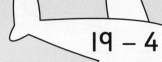

19 – 4

12 – 1

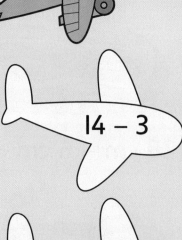

14 – 3

16 – 2

13 – 2

20
19
18
17
16
15
14
13
12
11
10
9
8
7
6
5
4
3
2

7 – 1

8 – 3

9 – 2

8 – 4

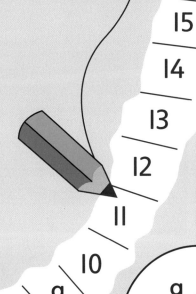

 Use a counter on the number line to make your own subtractions.

Count back along the line. Complete the subtractions by joining them to the line.

Write six subtractions with an answer of 10.

33

Taking away

54 cm − 2 cm = ☐ cm

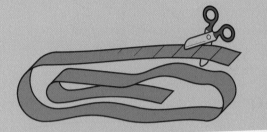

36 cm − 5 cm = ☐ cm

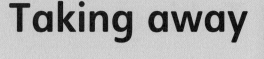

28 cm − 6 cm = ☐ cm

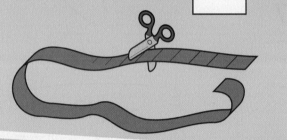

45 cm − 4 cm = ☐ cm

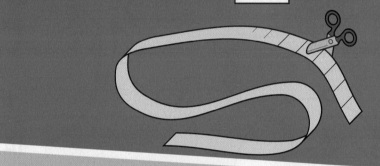

69 cm − 7 cm = ☐ cm

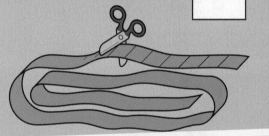

17 cm − 3 cm = ☐ cm

88 cm − 8 cm = ☐ cm

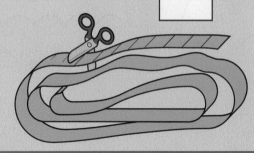

42 cm − 3 cm = ☐ cm

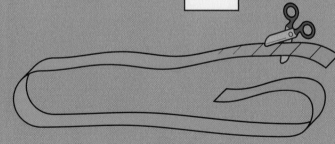

Cut a paper strip 10 squares long. Cut off some squares. How many left? Repeat.	Write the new lengths of the ribbons once they have been cut.	Cut a piece of string and measure it. How many times can you cut off 2 cm? Try.

Taking away

 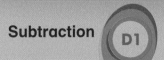

26 – ⬜ = 20   37 – ⬜ = 30

48 – ⬜ = 40   54 – ⬜ = 50   62 – ⬜ = 60

73 – ⬜ = 70   35 – ⬜ = ⬜

44 – ⬜ = ⬜   57 – ⬜ = ⬜

 Place a counter on a 100-square. Count back to the nearest multiple of 10.

Write the missing number so that the answer ends in 0 each time.

Take away one more than the number of units, for example 26 – 7. What is the pattern?

35

Taking away

15 16 17 18 19 20 21 22 23 24 25 26 27 2

23 – 6 = ☐   22 – 4 = ☐   21 – 5 = ☐

27 – 7 = ☐   25 – 6 = ☐   23 – 8 = ☐

32 33 34 35 36 37 38 39 40 41 42 43 44 45 46 47 48 49 50 5

36 – 3 = ☐   41 – 5 = ☐   44 – 6 = ☐

46 – 6 = ☐   50 – 7 = ☐   52 – 5 = ☐

Use a blank number track. Fill in the numbers and take away by counting back.

Use the number tracks to help you complete the subtractions.

Can you get from 32 to 19 in three subtractions?

Taking away

84 – 6 = ☐

54 – 6 = ☐

24 – 6 = ☐

85 – 8 = ☐

65 – 8 = ☐

45 – 8 = ☐

55 – 8 = ☐

72 – 5 = ☐

52 – 5 = ☐

32 – 5 = ☐

22 – 5 = ☐

91 – 4 = ☐

71 – 4 = ☐

41 – 4 = ☐

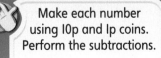

Make each number using 10p and 1p coins. Perform the subtractions.

Complete the subtraction in each link of the chains. What do you notice about each chain?

Create a chain of subtractions where the answers end in 9.

Doubling

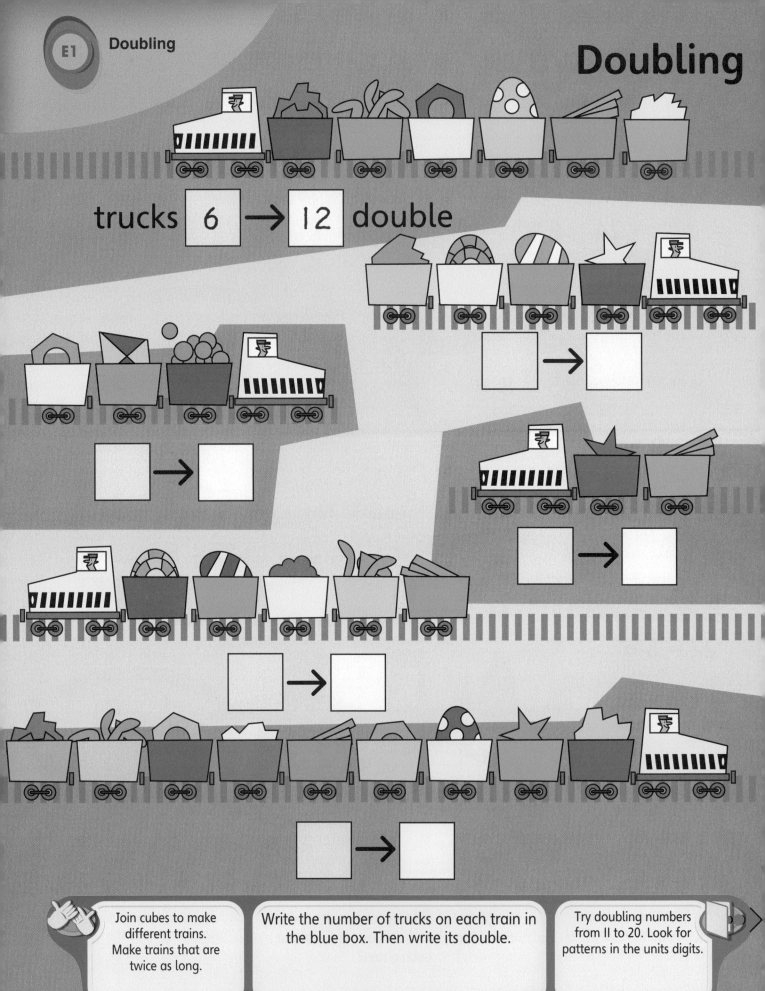

trucks 6 → 12 double

Join cubes to make different trains. Make trains that are twice as long.

Write the number of trucks on each train in the blue box. Then write its double.

Try doubling numbers from 11 to 20. Look for patterns in the units digits.

Halving

Use two sets of 1–20 number cards. Make pairs: one number half the other.

Join each duck to its half on the bank of the river.

Look at coins that are 10p or more. Explore the amount that is half. Which coins make the half?

39

Doubling

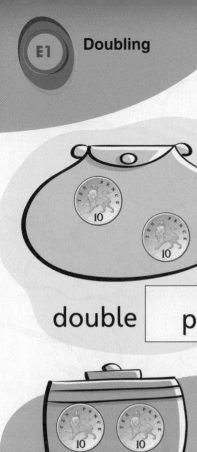

double ⬚ p

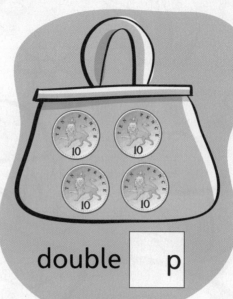

double ⬚ p

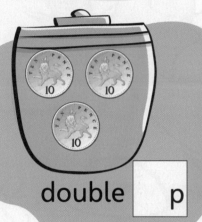

double ⬚ p

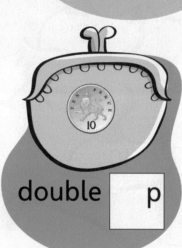

double ⬚ p

double ⬚ p

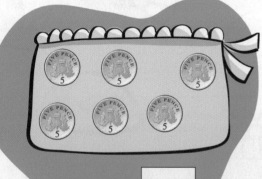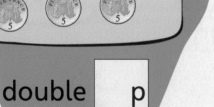

double ⬚ p

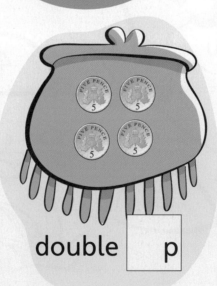

double ⬚ p

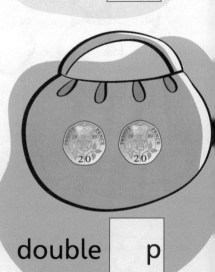

double ⬚ p

| Use real coins to help you double each amount. | Write double the amount in each purse. | Explore doubles of amounts more than 50p up to £2, using 10p coins. |

Doubling

 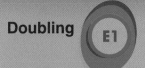

10p → 20p

30p →

25p →

5p →

40p →

35p →

20p →

45p →

15p →

50p →

 Use 10p and 5p coins to make pairs of piles of coins: one pile double the value of the other.

Double the amount in each machine at the 'Double your money' factory.

Tell your friend an amount that comes out of the machine, for example 50p. They tell you what went in.

41

Halving

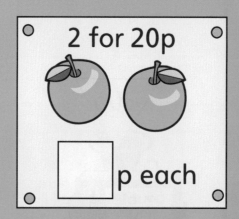

2 for 20p

[ ] p each

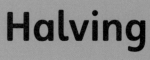

Special Offers!

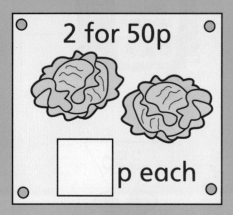

2 for 50p

[ ] p each

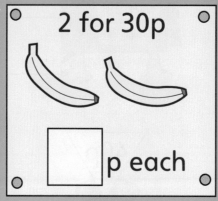

2 for 30p

[ ] p each

2 for 60p

[ ] p each

2 for 90p

[ ] p each

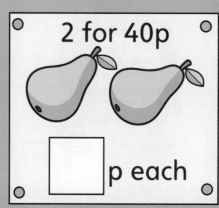

2 for 40p

[ ] p each

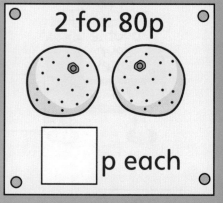

2 for 80p

[ ] p each

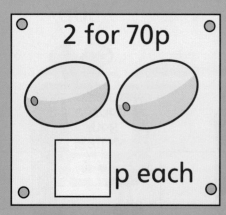

2 for 70p

[ ] p each

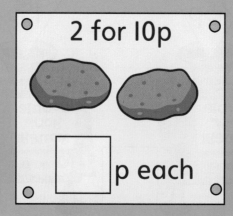

2 for 10p

[ ] p each

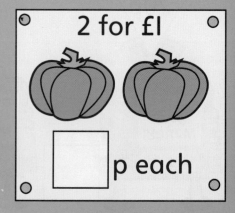

2 for £1

[ ] p each

Make each amount using 10p and 5p coins. Split this into two halves.

Write the cost of one of each fruit or vegetable.

Use repeated doubling to find the cost of eight of each item.

Adding coins

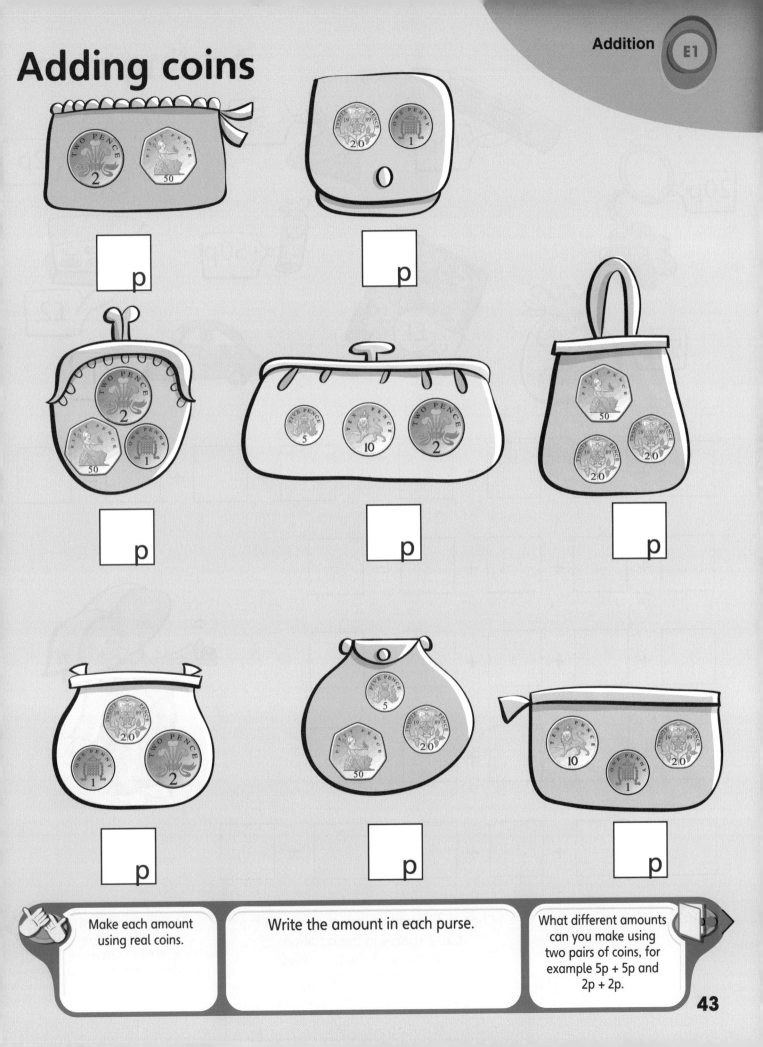

☐ p

☐ p

☐ p

☐ p

☐ p

☐ p

☐ p

☐ p

👉 Make each amount using real coins.

Write the amount in each purse.

What different amounts can you make using two pairs of coins, for example 5p + 5p and 2p + 2p.

Adding coins

$\square$ + $\square$ + $\square$ = $\square$ $\square$ + $\square$ + $\square$ = $\square$

$\square$ + $\square$ + $\square$ + $\square$ = $\square$

$\square$ + $\square$ + $\square$ + $\square$ = $\square$

$\square$ + $\square$ + $\square$ + $\square$ = $\square$

$\square$ + $\square$ + $\square$ + $\square$ + $\square$ = $\square$

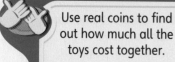 Use real coins to find out how much all the toys cost together.

Choose different toy prices to match the blank spaces in the additions. Find the total. Each set must be different.

Make a line of coins that is about 20 cm long. Which coins make this line worth the most?

Making amounts

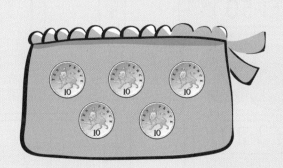

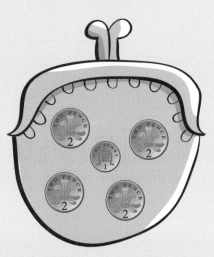

 Fill three purses with the same amount but using different coins in each.

Draw lines to join purses with the same amount.

Choose a coin. Add it to the sum of all the coins worth less than it, for example 5p + 2p + 1p. Repeat.

Making amounts

☐ + ☐   7p   12p   ☐ + ☐

☐ + ☐   25p   51p   ☐ + ☐

☐ + ☐   70p   £1·50   ☐ + ☐

☐ + ☐ + ☐   £1·15   £3·20   ☐ + ☐ + ☐

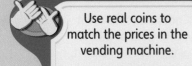

Use real coins to match the prices in the vending machine.

Write the coins needed to make each amount.

You have £1. What could you buy from the vending machine?

Making amounts

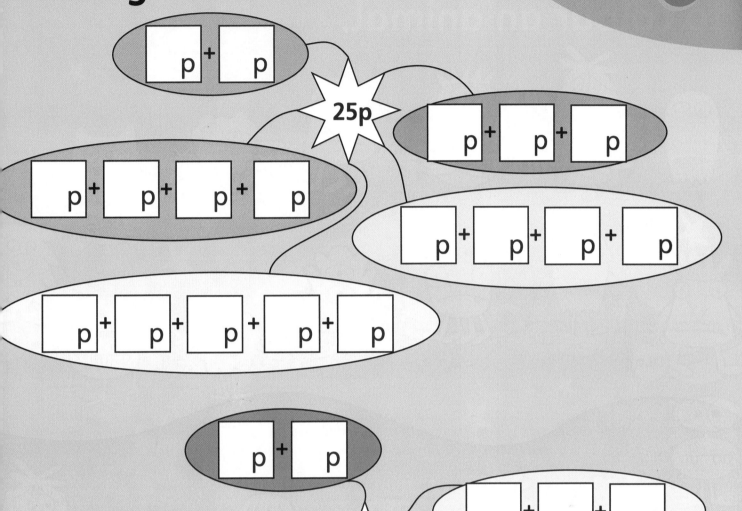

☐ p + ☐ p

25p

☐ p + ☐ p + ☐ p

☐ p + ☐ p + ☐ p + ☐ p

☐ p + ☐ p + ☐ p + ☐ p

☐ p + ☐ p + ☐ p + ☐ p + ☐ p

☐ p + ☐ p

30p

☐ p + ☐ p + ☐ p

☐ p + ☐ p + ☐ p

☐ p + ☐ p + ☐ p + ☐ p

☐ p + ☐ p + ☐ p + ☐ p + ☐ p

 Take a 20p coin. How many other ways can you find of making 20p?

Write different ways of making each amount.

Choose another amount. Make a puzzle like the ones on the page for a friend to solve.

Talk with your teacher about when to colour an animal.

The instructions at the foot of each page are written for teachers to explain to children. The core activity is written in the centre. The activities with the 👏 icon provide a practical activity, often requiring the children to do or make something, while the activities marked with ▶️ provide an activity for children who require more challenge.

Abacus Evolve Framework Edition

To find out more about Ginn products, plus free supporting resources, visit

www.ginn.co.uk
01865 888020

Ginn is an imprint of Pearson Education Limited, a company incorporated in England and Wales, having its registered office at Edinburgh Gate, Harlow, Essex, CM20 2JE. Registered company number: 872828

ISBN: 978 0602 57638 7 © Ginn 2007
First published 2007
Ninth impression 2010
Printed in Malaysia (CTP-VP)

Ginn
Part of Pearson

ISBN 978-0-602576-38-7
9 780602 576387

Abacus *evolve*

Workbook 2

2

One more, one less

| 75 | **76** | 77 |

| | 87 | |

| | 95 | |

| | **83** | |

| | 8 | |

| | 106 | |

| | 16 | |

| | 22 | |

| | 124 | |

| | 101 | |

| | 40 | |

| | 99 | |

| | 112 | |

Say a number. Your partner says the number one less; you say the number one more. Swap roles.

Write the number one less and the number one more on each strip.

Write sequences of three numbers where the middle number has two digits the same.

Ten more, ten less

13	14				
23	24	25	26	27	
33	34	35	36	37	38
43	44	45	46	47	48

34

23

26

45

52

28

61

82

73

117

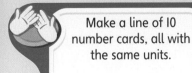 Make a line of 10 number cards, all with the same units.

Write the missing numbers, counting in 10s.

Describe moving from 23 to 67 on a number grid using '10 more' and 'one more'.

3

Counting in 100s

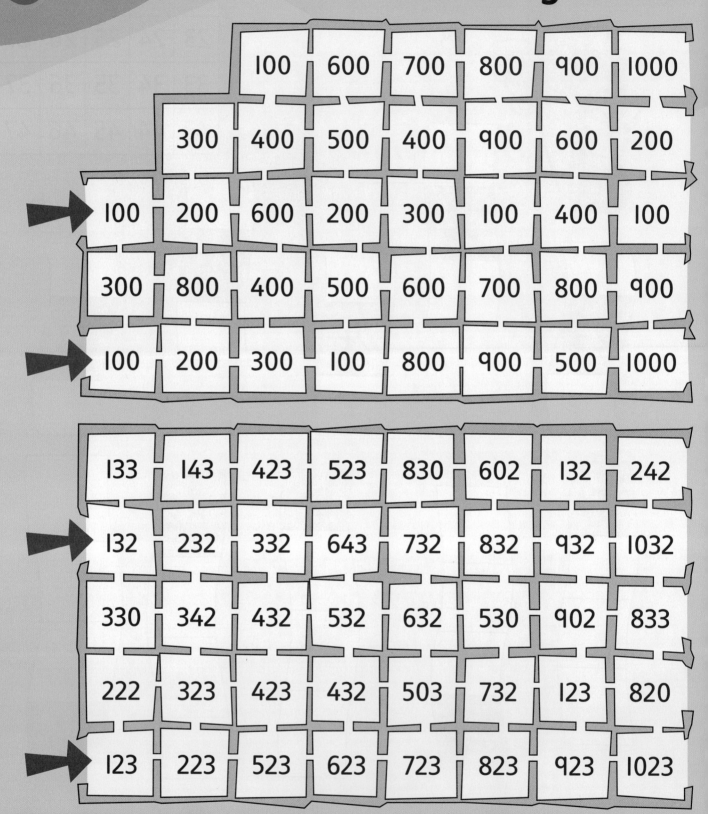

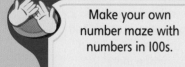

| Make your own number maze with numbers in 100s. | Count in 100s to find a way through the maze. Start from the arrow and colour boxes until you reach the other side. | Make your own number maze, counting in 50s. |

Odd and even

2	4	6	8	10
12				20
		26		
			38	
	44			

Even numbers

1	3	5	7
11		15	
			27
	33		
		45	

Odd numbers

Make up a chant for odd or even numbers: *Two, four, six, eight. Who do we appreciate…*

Fill in the missing even numbers and the missing odd numbers.

Write some odd 2-digit numbers that are still odd when you reverse the digits.

5

Odd and even

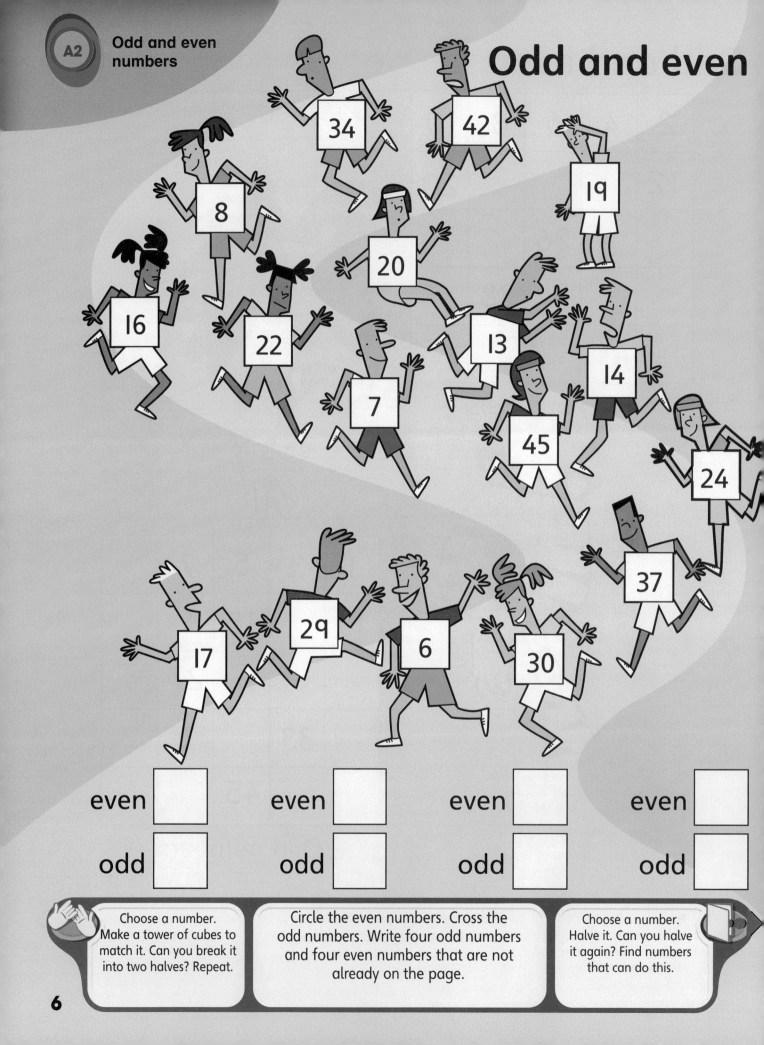

even

odd

even

odd

even

odd

even

odd

Choose a number. Make a tower of cubes to match it. Can you break it into two halves? Repeat.

Circle the even numbers. Cross the odd numbers. Write four odd numbers and four even numbers that are not already on the page.

Choose a number. Halve it. Can you halve it again? Find numbers that can do this.